THE PROBLEM OF SUSAN AND OTHER STORIES

NEIL GAIMAN
Stories and Words

P. CRAIG RUSSELL
Adaptation and Art *(The Problem of Susan, Locks)*
Script and Layout *(October in the Chair)*

SCOTT HAMPTON
Art *(October in the Chair)*

PAUL CHADWICK
Art *(The Day the Saucers Came)*

LOVERN KINDZIERSKI
Colours *(The Problem of Susan, Locks)*

GALEN SHOWMAN
Letters *(The Problem of Susan, Locks)*

RICK PARKER
Letters *(October in the Chair)*

GASPAR SALADINO
Letters *(The Day the Saucers Came)*

HEADLINE

Special thanks to Diana Schutz

Names: Gaiman, Neil, author. | Russell, P. Craig, artist. | Hampton, Scott, artist. | Chadwick, Paul (Paul H), artist. | Kindzierski, Lovern, 1954- colourist. | Showman, Galen, letterer. | Parker, Rick, 1946- letterer. | Saladino, Gaspar, letterer

Title: The Problem of Susan and Other Stories / Neil Gaiman, story and words; P. Craig Russell, art and adaptation (*The Problem of Susan, Locks*); Scott Hampton, art (*October in the Chair*); Paul Chadwick, art (*The Day the Saucers Came*); Lovern Kindierski, colours (*The Problem of Susan, Locks*); Galen Showman, letters (*The Problem of Susan, Locks*); Rick Parker, letters (*October in the Chair*); Gaspar Saladino, letters (*The Day the Saucers Came*)

The Day the Saucers Came previously collected in *Dark Horse Presents* Vol. 2 #21

First published in the US in 2019 by Dark Horse Books
A division of Dark Horse Comics, Inc.

First published in Great Britain in 2019 by
HEADLINE PUBLISHING GROUP

1

Cataloguing in Publication Data is available from the British Library

ISBN 978 1 4722 6293 6

Designer: Sarah Terry

Printed and bound in Italy by L.E.G.O. S.p.A

Headline's policy is to use papers that are natural, renewable and recyclable products and made from wood grown in sustainable forests. The logging and manufacturing processes are expected to conform to the environmental regulations of the country of origin.

HEADLINE PUBLISHING GROUP
An Hachette UK Company
Carmelite House
50 Victoria Embankment
London EC4Y 0DZ

www.headline.co.uk
www.hachette.co.uk

THE PROBLEM OF SUSAN

AND OTHER STORIES

THE PROBLEM OF SUSAN

THE
PROBLEM
of
SUSAN

SHE HAS THE DREAM AGAIN THAT NIGHT.

THE CHILDREN CANNOT MAKE OUT ANY OF THEIR WORDS...

...NOT HER COLD ANGER...

...NOR THE LION'S THRUM-DEEP REPLIES.

THE WITCH'S HAIR IS BLACK AND SHINY...

...HER LIPS ARE RED.

IN HER DREAM SHE NOTICES THESE THINGS.

THEY WILL FINISH THEIR CONVERSATION SOON, THE LION AND THE WITCH...

HERE ARE THINGS ABOUT HERSELF THAT THE PROFESSOR DESPISES. HER SMELL, FOR EXAMPLE. SHE SMELLS LIKE HER GRANDMOTHER SMELLED. AN OLD WOMAN SMELL.

SO ON WAKING SHE BATHES IN SCENTED WATER...

...AND, NAKED AND TOWEL-DRIED, DABS SEVERAL DROPS OF CHANEL TOILET WATER BENEATH HER ARMS AND ON HER NECK.

IT IS, SHE BELIEVES, HER SOLE EXTRAVAGANCE.

TODAY SHE DRESSES IN WHAT SHE THINKS OF AS HER INTERVIEW CLOTHES, AS OPPOSED TO HER LECTURE CLOTHES OR HER KNOCKING-ABOUT-THE-HOUSE CLOTHES.

THAT HAD BEEN AT A *LITERARY MONTHLY* CHRISTMAS PARTY AND HE HAD REMINDED HER OF NOTHING SO MUCH AS...

A CARICATURE OF AN OWL.

IN THE PHOTOGRAPH, HE IS VERY BEAUTIFUL. HE LOOKS WILD, AND NOBLE.

SHE HAD SPENT AN EVENING ONCE KISSING HIM IN A SUMMER HOUSE, ALTHOUGH SHE CANNOT REMEMBER FOR THE LIFE OF HER IN WHICH GARDEN THE SUMMER HOUSE HAD BELONGED.

IT MUST HAVE BEEN CHARLES AND NADIA REID'S HOUSE IN THE COUNTRY.

WHICH MEANS IT WAS BEFORE NADIA RAN AWAY WITH THAT SCOTTISH ARTIST AND CHARLES TOOK ME WITH HIM TO SPAIN.

SPAIN SEEMED SO EXOTIC AND DANGEROUS IN THOSE DAYS.

YOU ASKED ME TO MARRY YOU.

WHY DID I SAY NO?

YOU WERE A PLEASANT-ENOUGH YOUNG MAN.

HE TOOK WHAT WAS LEFT OF HER VIRGINITY ON A SPANISH BEACH, ON A WARM SUMMER NIGHT.

I WAS TWENTY YEARS OLD AND THOUGHT MYSELF SO OLD.

HER FIRST THOUGHT IS HOW YOUNG THE GIRL LOOKS.

JUST LIKE IN LEWIS'S *NARNIA* BOOKS.

...AND GRETA IMMEDIATELY FEELS LIKE A FOOL, AN INSENSITIVE FOOL.

I'M SORRY. THAT WAS A TERRIBLE THING TO SAY, WASN'T IT?

WAS IT, DEAR?

IT'S JUST I REMEMBER THAT SEQUENCE SO VIVIDLY, IN *THE LAST BATTLE*, WHERE YOU LEARN THERE WAS A TRAIN CRASH ON THE WAY BACK TO SCHOOL, AND EVERYONE WAS KILLED.

EXCEPT FOR SUSAN, OF COURSE.

MORE TEA, DEAR?

GRETA KNOWS THAT SHE SHOULD LEAVE THE SUBJECT, BUT...

YOU KNOW, THAT USED TO MAKE ME SO ANGRY.

WHAT DID, DEAR?

SUSAN.

THERE MUST HAVE BEEN SOMETHING ELSE WRONG WITH SUSAN, SOMETHING THEY DIDN'T TELL US. OTHERWISE SHE WOULDN'T HAVE BEEN DAMNED LIKE THAT-- DENIED THE HEAVEN OF FURTHER UP AND FURTHER IN.

" I MEAN, ALL THE PEOPLE SHE HAD EVER CARED FOR HAD GONE ON TO THEIR REWARD, IN A WORLD OF MAGIC AND WATER- FALLS AND JOY.

AND SHE WAS LEFT BEHIND. "

I DON'T KNOW ABOUT THE GIRL IN THE BOOKS. BUT REMAINING BEHIND WOULD ALSO HAVE MEANT THAT SHE WAS AVAILABLE TO IDENTIFY HER BROTHERS' AND HER LITTLE SISTER'S BODIES.

THERE WERE A LOT OF PEOPLE DEAD IN THAT CRASH.

" I WAS TAKEN TO A NEARBY SCHOOL -- IT WAS THE FIRST DAY OF TERM, AND THEY HAD TAKEN THE BODIES THERE.

"MY OLDER BROTHER LOOKED OKAY.

"LIKE HE WAS ASLEEP

I SUPPOSE SUSAN WOULD HAVE SEEN THEIR BODIES, AND THOUGHT, THEY'RE O HOLIDAYS NOW. ROMP IN MEADOWS WITH TALKING ANIMALS, WORLD WITHOUT END.

" THE OTHER TWO WERE A BIT MESSIER. "

THAT NIGHT, THE PROFESSOR CLIMBS THE STAIRS OF HER HOUSE, SLOWLY, PAINSTAKINGLY, FLOOR BY FLOOR.

SHE MAKES UP A BED IN THE SPARE BEDROOM, AT THE BACK...

SHE PLACES A VASE ON THE DRESSING TABLE, CONTAINING PURPLE RHODODENDRON FLOWERS, STICKY AND VULGAR...

...TAKES FROM A BOX IN THE WARDROBE A PLASTIC SHOPPING BAG CONTAINING FOUR OLD PHOTOGRAPHIC ALBUMS...

...AND CLIMBS INTO THE BED THAT WAS HERS AS A CHILD.

I AM SATISFIED WITH THE TERMS OF OUR AGREEMENT.

YOU TAKE THE GIRLS...

...FOR MYSELF, I SHALL HAVE THE BOYS.

THE BEAST IS UPON HER BEFORE SHE HAS COVERED A DOZEN PACES.

THE LION EATS ALL OF HER EXCEPT HER HEAD, IN HER DREAM.

HE LEAVES THE HEAD, AND ONE OF HER HANDS.

SHE WISHES THAT HE HAD EATEN HER HEAD, THEN SHE WOULD NOT HAVE TO LOOK...

...DEAD EYELIDS CANNOT BE CLOSED...

BEING DEAD, THE EYES IN THE HEAD ON THE GRASS CANNOT LOOK AWAY. BEING DEAD, THEY MISS NOTHING.

AND WHEN THE TWO OF THEM ARE DONE, SWEATY AND STICKY AND SATED...

...ONLY THEN DOES THE LION AMBLE OVER TO THE HEAD ON THE GRASS...

...AND DEVOUR IT IN ITS HUGE MOUTH...

...AND IT IS THEN, ONLY THEN,

LOCKS

locks

WE OWE IT TO EACH OTHER TO TELL STORIES, AS PEOPLE SIMPLY, NOT AS FATHER AND DAUGHTER. I TELL IT TO YOU FOR THE HUNDREDTH TIME:

THERE WAS A LITTLE GIRL, CALLED GOLDILOCKS, FOR HER HAIR WAS LONG AND GOLDEN...

AND SHE WAS WALKING IN THE WOOD AND SHE SAW...

COWS.

YOU SAY IT WITH CERTAINTY, REMEMBERING THE STRAYED HEIFERS WE SAW IN THE WOODS BEHIND THE HOUSE, LAST MONTH.

WELL, YES, PERHAPS SHE SAW COWS, BUT ALSO SHE SAW A HOUSE.

--A GREAT BIG HOUSE--

YOU TELL ME.

"NO, A LITTLE HOUSE, ALL PAINTED, NEAT AND TIDY."

"A GREAT BIG HOUSE."

YOU HAVE THE CONVICTION OF ALL TWO-YEAR-OLDS. I WISH I HAD SUCH CERTITUDE.

"AH. YES. A GREAT BIG HOUSE. AND SHE WENT IN..."

I REMEMBER, AS I TELL IT, THAT THE LOCKS OF SOUTHEY'S HEROINE HAD SILVERED WITH AGE. THE OLD WOMAN AND THE THREE BEARS...

PERHAPS THEY HAD BEEN GOLDEN ONCE, WHEN SHE WAS A CHILD.

AND NOW, WE ARE ALREADY UP TO THE PORRIDGE...

AND IT WAS TOO-- HOT!

AND IT WAS TOO-- COLD!

AND THEN IT WAS, WE CHORUS...

JUST RIGHT.

THE PORRIDGE IS EATEN, THE BABY'S CHAIR IS SHATTERED.

GOLDILOCKS GOES UPSTAIRS, EXAMINES BEDS, AND SLEEPS, UNWISELY.

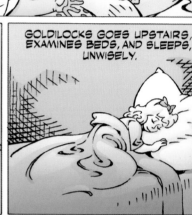

BUT THEN THE BEARS RETURN.

!

REMEMBERING SOUTHEY STILL, I DO THE VOICES: FATHER BEAR'S GRUFF BOOM SCARES YOU, AND YOU DELIGHT IN IT.

WHEN I WAS A SMALL CHILD AND HEARD THE TALE, IF I WAS ANYONE I WAS BABY BEAR, MY PORRIDGE EATEN AND MY CHAIR DESTROYED, MY BED INHABITED BY SOME STRANGE GIRL.

YOU GIGGLE WHEN I DO THE BABY'S WAIL...

SOMEONE'S BEEN EATING MY PORRIDGE, AND THEY'VE EATEN IT...

ALL UP...

YOU SAY. A RESPONSE IT IS, OR AN AMEN.

THE BEARS GO UPSTAIRS HESITANTLY, THEIR HOUSE NOW FEELS DESECRATED. THEY REALIZE WHAT LOCKS ARE FOR.

THEY REACH THE BEDROOM.

"SOMEONE'S BEEN SLEEPING IN MY BED."

AND HERE I HESITATE, ECHOES OF OLD JOKES, SOFT-CORE CARTOONS, CRUDE HEADLINES, IN MY HEAD.

ONE DAY YOUR MOUTH WILL CURL AT THAT LINE. A LOSS OF INTEREST. LATER, INNOCENCE. INNOCENCE, AS IF IT WERE A COMMODITY.

And if I could,

—MY FATHER WROTE TO ME, HUGE AS A BEAR HIMSELF, WHEN I WAS YOUNGER . . .

I WOULD DOWER YOU WITH EXPERIENCE, WITHOUT EXPERIENCE.

AND I, IN MY TURN, WOULD PASS THAT ON TO YOU. BUT WE MAKE OUR OWN MISTAKES.

WE SLEEP - UNWISELY.

THE REPETITION ECHOES DOWN THE YEARS. WHEN YOUR CHILDREN GROW, WHEN YOUR DARK LOCKS BEGIN TO SILVER, WHEN YOU ARE AN OLD WOMAN, ALONE WITH YOUR THREE BEARS, WHAT WILL YOU SEE? WHAT STORIES WILL YOU TELL?

"AND THEN GOLDILOCKS JUMPED OUT OF THE WINDOW AND SHE RAN--"

TOGETHER, NOW:

ALL THE WAY HOME.

AND THEN YOU SAY...

AGAIN. AGAIN. AGAIN.

WE OWE IT TO EACH OTHER TO TELL STORIES.

THESE DAYS, MY SYMPATHY'S WITH FATHER BEAR.

BEFORE I LEAVE MY HOUSE I LOCK THE DOOR...

...AND CHECK EACH BED AND CHAIR ON MY RETURN.

AGAIN.

AGAIN.

AGAIN.

END

OCTOBER IN
THE CHAIR

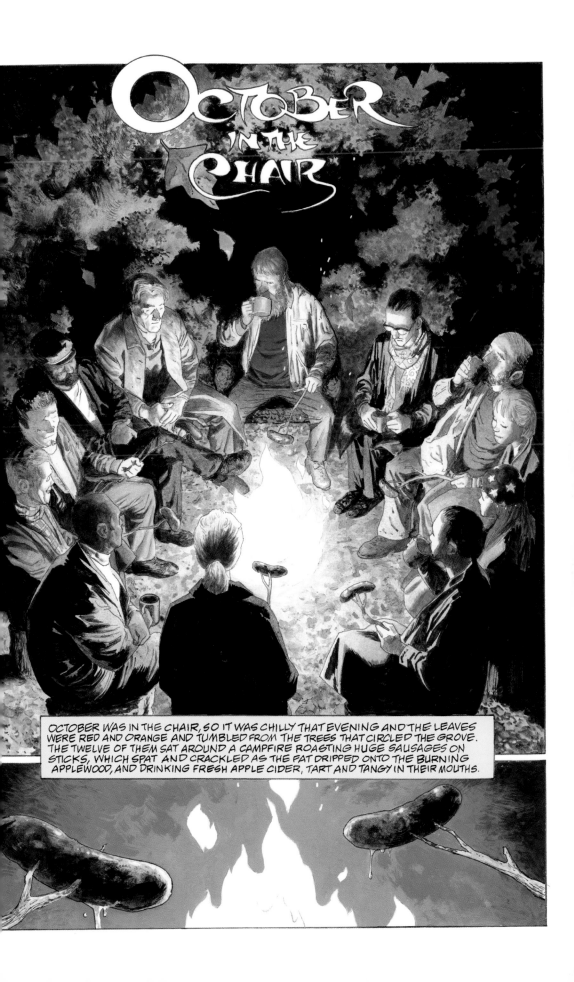

OCTOBER IN THE CHAIR

OCTOBER WAS IN THE CHAIR, SO IT WAS CHILLY THAT EVENING AND THE LEAVES
WERE RED AND ORANGE AND TUMBLED FROM THE TREES THAT CIRCLED THE GROVE.
THE TWELVE OF THEM SAT AROUND A CAMPFIRE ROASTING HUGE SAUSAGES ON
STICKS, WHICH SPAT AND CRACKLED AS THE FAT DRIPPED ONTO THE BURNING
APPLEWOOD, AND DRINKING FRESH APPLE CIDER, TART AND TANGY IN THEIR MOUTHS.

April

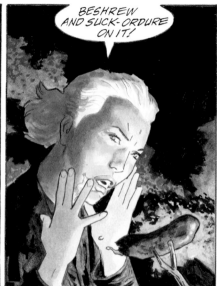

BESHREW AND SUCK-ORDURE ON IT!

AHHH

HEH.

HEH HEH HEH.

HERE YOU GO.

MA

THANKS. THE CURSED BAG OF INNARDS BURNED ME. I'LL HAVE A BLISTER THERE TOMORROW.

September

YOU ARE SUCH A HYPOCHONDRIAC.

AND SUCH LANGUAGE.

May

LAY OFF HER. SHE'S SENSITIVE.

OH, PUH-LEEZE SPARE ME.

OKAY!

WHO WANTS TO BEGIN?

≡AHEM≡

LAURENT DELISLE WAS THE FINEST CHEF IN ALL OF SEATTLE...

"...AT LEAST, LAURENT DELISLE THOUGHT SO, AND THE THREE MICHELIN STARS ON HIS DOOR CONFIRMED HIM IN HIS OPINION.

"HE WAS A REMARKABLE CHEF, IT IS TRUE-- HIS MINCED LAMB BRIOCHE HAD WON SEVERAL AWARDS.

"HIS SMOKED QUAIL AND WHITE TRUFFLE RAVIOLI HAD BEEN DESCRIBED IN THE GASTRONOME AS..."

THE TENTH WONDER OF THE WORLD!

"BUT IT WAS HIS WINE CELLAR... AH, HIS WINE CELLAR, THAT WAS THE SOURCE OF HIS PRIDE AND HIS PASSION."

I UNDERSTAND THAT. THE LAST OF THE WHITE GRAPES ARE HARVESTED IN *ME*. I APPRECIATE FINE WINES, THE AROMA, THE TASTE.

"THE TREASURE-- THE JEWEL-- THE RAREST OF THE *RARE*-- AND THE *NE PLUS ULTRA* OF HIS TEMPERATURE-CONTROLLED WINE CELLAR WAS A BOTTLE OF 1902 *CHATEAU LAFITTE*."

EXCUSE N

AUGUST

IS THIS THE ONE WHERE SOME RICH DUDE BUYS THE WINE TO GO WITH THE DINNER, AND THE CHEF DECIDES THAT THE DINNER THE RICH DUDE ORDERED ISN'T GOOD ENOUGH FOR THE WINE, SO HE SENDS OUT A DIFFERENT DINNER, AND THE GUY TAKES ONE MOUTHFUL AND HE'S GOT, LIKE, SOME RARE ALLERGY AND HE JUST DIES LIKE THAT, AND THE WINE NEVER GETS DRUNK AFTER ALL?

YES?

...ECAUSE IF IT ..S, YOU TOLD ..T BEFORE.

YEARS AGO.

DUMB STORY THEN. DUMB STORY NOW.

OBVIOUSLY, PATHOS AND CULTURE ARE NOT TO EVERYONE'S TASTE. *SOME* PEOPLE PREFER THEIR BARBECUES AND BEER, AND SOME OF US LIKE...

WELL, I HATE TO SAY THIS, BUT HE DOES HAVE A POINT. IT HAS TO BE A NEW STORY.

I'M DONE.

JUNE

I HAVE ONE...

EN ES.

FOUR Nays.

I CANNOT BELIEVE THIS IS HAPPENING

July

I DON'T HAVE ANYTHING PERSONAL ON THIS. IT'S PURELY PROCEDURAL. WE SHOULDN'T BE SETTING PRECEDENTS.

IT'S SETTLED THEN. IS THERE ANYTHING ANYONE WOULD LIKE TO SAY BEFORE I BEGIN?

umm... YES. SOME-TIMES...

"... SOMETIMES I THINK SOMEBODY'S WATCHING US FROM THE WOODS, AND THEN I LOOK UP AND THERE ISN'T ANYBODY THERE."

BUT I STILL THINK IT.

THAT'S BECAUSE YOU'RE CRAZY.

MMMM...... THAT'S OUR APRIL. SHE'S SENSITIVE BUT SHE'S STILL THE CRUELEST...

OCTOBER STRETCHED IN HIS CHAIR. HE CRACKED A COBNUT WITH HIS TEETH, PULLED OUT THE KERNEL, AND THREW THE FRAGMENTS OF SHELL INTO THE FIRE, WHERE THEY HISSED AND SPAT AND POPPED. AND HE BEGAN.

ENOUGH!

THERE WAS A BOY...

"THERE WAS A BOY WHO WAS MISERABLE AT HOME, ALTHOUGH THEY DID NOT BEAT HIM. HE DID NOT FIT WELL, NOT HIS FAMILY, HIS TOWN, NOR EVEN HIS LIFE.

"HE HAD TWO BROTHERS, WHO WERE TWINS, OLDER THAN HE WAS, AND WHO HURT HIM OR IGNORED HIM, AND WERE POPULAR.

"THEY PLAYED FOOTBALL: SOME GAMES, ONE TWIN WOULD SCORE MORE AND BE THE HERO, AND SOME GAMES, THE OTHER WOULD.

THEIR LITTLE BROTHER DID NOT PLAY FOOTBALL. THEY HAD A NAME FOR HIM,

"THEY CALLED HIM THE RUNT.

"THEY HAD CALLED HIM THE RUNT SINCE HE WAS A BABY, AND AT FIRST THEIR MOTHER AND FATHER HAD CHIDED THEM FOR IT."

BUT HE *IS* THE RUNT OF THE LITTER. LOOK AT *HIM*. LOOK AT *US*.

"THE BOYS WERE SIX WHEN THEY SAID THIS.

"THEIR PARENTS THOUGHT IT WAS CUTE.

"SO PRETTY SOON, THE ONLY PERSON WHO CALLED HIM DONALD WAS HIS GRANDMOTHER WHEN SHE TELEPHONED HIM ON HIS BIRTHDAY.

OW, PERHAPS
CAUSE
MES HAVE
WER, HE
AS A RUNT...

"...SKINNY AND SMALL AND NERVOUS.

"HE HAD BEEN BORN WITH A RUNNY NOSE, AND IT HAD NOT STOPPED RUNNING IN A DECADE.

AT MEALTIMES, IF THE TWINS LIKED THE FOOD, THEY WOULD STEAL HIS.

"IF THEY DID NOT, THEY WOULD CONTRIVE TO PLACE THEIR FOOD ON HIS PLATE AND HE'D FIND HIMSELF IN TROUBLE FOR LEAVING GOOD FOOD UNEATEN.

THEIR FATHER NEVER MISSED A FOOTBALL GAME, AND WOULD BUY AN ICE CREAM AFTERWARD FOR THE TWIN WHO HAD SCORED THE MOST, AND A CONSOLATION ICE CREAM FOR THE OTHER TWIN, WHO HADN'T.

"THEIR MOTHER DESCRIBED HERSELF AS A NEWSPAPERWOMAN, ALTHOUGH SHE MOSTLY SOLD SUBSCRIPTIONS: SHE HAD GONE BACK TO WORK FULL TIME ONCE THE TWINS WERE CAPABLE OF TAKING CARE OF THEMSELVES.

"THE OTHER KIDS IN THE BOY'S CLASS CALLED HIM DONALD UNTIL WORD TRICKLED DOWN THAT HIS BROTHERS CALLED HIM..."

RUNT.

"HIS TEACHERS RARELY CALLED HIM ANYTHING AT ALL, ALTHOUGH THEY COULD SOMETIMES BE HEARD TO SAY..."

IT'S A PITY HE DOESN'T HAVE THE PLUCK OR THE IMAGINATION OR LIFE OF HIS BROTHERS.

"THE RUNT COULD NOT HAVE TOLD YOU WHEN HE FIRST DECIDED TO RUN AWAY.

"BY THE TIME HE ADMITTED TO HIMSELF HE WAS LEAVING, HE HAD A LARGE TUPPERWARE CONTAINER HIDDEN BENEATH A PLASTIC SHEET BEHIND THE GARAGE.

"IT CONTAINED THREE MARS BARS, TWO MILKY WAYS, A BAG OF NUTS, A SMALL BAG OF LICORICE, A FLASHLIGHT, SEVERAL COMICS, AN UNOPENED BAG OF BEEF JERKY, AND THIRTY-SEVEN DOLLARS, MOST OF IT IN QUARTERS.

"HE DID NOT LIKE THE TASTE OF BEEF JERKY, BUT HE HAD READ THAT EXPLORERS HAD SURVIVED FOR WEEKS ON NOTHING ELSE.

"IT WAS WHEN HE PUT THE PACKET OF BEEF JERKY INTO THE TUPPERWARE BOX AND PRESSED THE LID DOWN WITH A POP THAT HE KNEW HE WAS GOING TO HAVE TO RUN AWAY.

E HAD READ BOOKS, NEWSPAPERS, AND
AGAZINES. HE KNEW THAT IF YOU RAN AWAY
OU SOMETIMES MET BAD PEOPLE.

"BUT HE HAD ALSO READ FAIRY TALES, SO HE KNEW
THAT THERE WERE KIND PEOPLE OUT THERE.
SIDE BY SIDE WITH THE MONSTERS.

LL THROUGH SEPTEMBER HE PUT OFF
EAVING. IT TOOK A REALLY BAD FRIDAY
URING THE COURSE OF WHICH BOTH OF
IS BROTHERS SAT ON HIM.

"THE
ONE
WHO
SAT
ON
HIS
FACE
BROKE
WIND.

"HE DECIDED
THAT WHATEVER
MONSTERS WERE
WAITING OUT IN
THE WORLD
WOULD BE
BEARABLE,
PERHAPS EVEN
PREFERABLE.

"SATURDAY, HIS BROTHERS WERE
MEANT TO BE LOOKING AFTER HIM,
BUT SOON THEY WENT INTO TOWN
TO SEE A GIRL THEY LIKED.

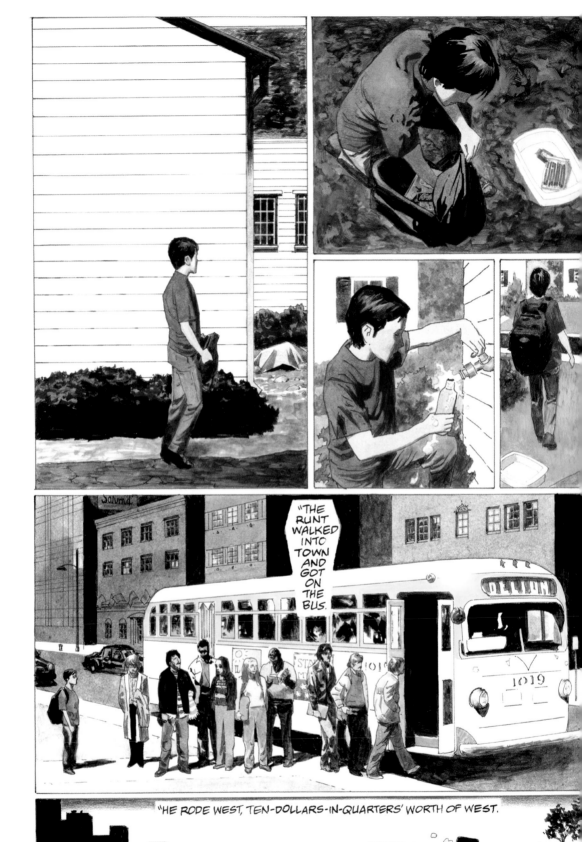

"THE RUNT WALKED INTO TOWN AND GOT ON THE BUS.

"HE RODE WEST, TEN-DOLLARS-IN-QUARTERS' WORTH OF WEST.

"THEN HE GOT OFF THE BUS.

"HE HAD THOUGHT THAT ONCE HE GOT OUT OF TOWN HE WOULD SEE SPRINGS OF FRESH WATER EVERYWHERE BUT THERE WERE NONE TO BE FOUND. HE REMEMBERED SOMETHING HE HAD BEEN TOLD IN SCHOOL..."

IN THE END, ALL RIVERS FLOW INTO THE SEA.

I'VE NEVER BEEN TO THE SEASHORE.

"HE WONDERED IF THEY WERE LOOKING FOR HIM YET.

"HE IMAGINED POLICE CARS AND HELICOPTERS AND DOGS, ALL TRYING TO FIND HIM."

BUT THEY WON'T.

" I'LL MAKE IT TO THE SEA.

THEY'LL BE MISSING ME BY NOW.

THEY'LL BE WORRIED.

"HE IMAGINED HIMSELF COMING HOME IN A FEW YEARS' TIME. THE DELIGHT ON HIS FAMILY'S FACES AS HE WALKED UP THE PATH TO HOME.

THEIR WELCOME.

"THEIR LOVE."

WHERE DO YOU COME FROM?

WHO'S THERE?

"SOMETHING HE HAD TAKEN FOR A SHADOW MOVED, BESIDE A TREE ON THE EDGE OF THE PASTURE, AND HE SAW A BOY OF HIS OWN AGE."

YOU CAN HIDE IN THE TREES AND GO INTO THE HOUSES AND JUMP OUT.

ARE THEY LIKE THAT FARMHOUSE UP THERE? THE HOUSES? I DON'T WANT TO GO IN THEM IF THEY ARE.

NO, NOBODY GOES IN THEM, EXCEPT FOR ME. AND SOME ANIMALS SOMETIMES. I'M THE ONLY KID AROUND HERE.

MAYBE WE CAN GO DOWN AND PLAY IN THEM.

COO

"IT WAS A PERFECT OCTOBER NIGHT: ALMOST AS WARM AS SUMMER AND THE HARVEST MOON DOMINATED THE SKY. YOU COULD SEE EVERYTHING."

WHICH ONE IS YOURS?

HERE.

DEARLY DEPARTED WILL NEVER BE FORG

FORGOTTEN I'D WAGER!

YEAH, THAT'S WHAT I'D SAY, TOO.

LET'S GO.

"THEY WENT DOWN A GULLY AND INTO WHAT REMAINED OF THE OLD TOWN.

"TREES GREW THROUGH HOUSES, AND BUILDINGS HAD FALLEN IN ON THEMSELVES, BUT IT WASN'T SCARY."

"THEY EXPLORED."

"THEY PLAYED HIDE AND SEEK."

I CAN SEE PRETTY GOOD BY MOONLIGHT. EVEN INSIDE. I DIDN'T KNOW IT WAS SO EASY.

AFTER A WHILE YOU GET GOOD AT SEEING, EVEN WHEN THERE AIN'T ANY MOON-LIGHT.

HOW DID YOU DIE?

I GOT SICK. MY MAW CRIED AND CARRIED ON SOMETHING FIERCE.

THEN I DIED.

IF I STAYED HERE WITH YOU, WOULD I HAVE TO BE DEAD, TOO?

WELL, YEAH, I GUESS.

WHAT'S IT LIKE? BEING DEAD?

I DON'T MIND IT. WORST THING IS NOT HAVING ANYONE TO PLAY WITH.

BUT THE PEOPLE UP IN THAT MEADOW. DON'T THEY EVER PLAY WITH YOU?

NOPE. MOSTLY THEY SLEEP. THEY CAN'T BE BOTHERED WITH ME.

YOU SEE THAT TREE?

YEAH?

YOU WANT TO CLIMB IT?

IT LOOKS KIND OF HIGH.

IT IS. BUT IT'S EASY TO CLIMB. I'LL SHOW YOU.

"IT WAS EASY TO CLIMB, AND THE BOYS WENT UP THE BIG BEECH LIKE A COUPLE OF MONKEYS OR PIRATES OR WARRIORS.

FROM THE TOP OF THE TREE ONE COULD SEE THE WHOLE WORLD.

THE SKY WAS STARTING TO LIGHTEN, JUST A HAIR IN THE EAST."

ME TOO. WHAT ARE YOU GOING TO DO NOW?

THIS WAS THE BEST DAY I EVER HAD.

I DON'T KNOW.

"HE IMAGINED HIMSELF GOING ON ACROSS THE WORLD, ALL THE WAY TO THE SEA. HE IMAGINED GROWING UP, AND GROWING OLDER. SOMEWHERE IN THERE, HE WOULD GROW FABULOUSLY WEALTHY.

...ND THEN HE WOULD GO BACK TO THE HOUSE ...TH THE TWINS IN IT, AND HE WOULD DRIVE UP ...O THE DOOR IN HIS WONDERFUL CAR.

"HE WOULD BUY THEM ALL, THE TWINS, HIS PARENTS, A MEAL AT THE FINEST RESTAURANT IN THE CITY.

...ND THEY WOULD TELL HIM HOW BADLY THEY HAD ...STREATED HIM. THEY APOLOGIZED AND WEPT ...D THROUGH IT ALL HE SAID NOTHING.

"AND THEN HE WOULD GIVE EACH OF THEM A GIFT. AND AFTERWARD HE WOULD LEAVE THEIR LIVES ONCE MORE, THIS TIME FOR GOOD.

"IT WAS A FINE DREAM.

"IN REALITY, HE KNEW HE WOULD KEEP WALKING, AND BE FOUND TOMORROW OR THE DAY AFTER THAT.

"HE WOULD GO HOME...

"...AND BE YELLED AT...

"AND EVERYTHING WOULD BE THE SAME AS IT EVER WAS...

"...AND DAY AFTER DAY,...

"...HOUR AFTER HOUR UNTIL THE END OF TIME,...

"...HE'D STILL BE THE RUNT."

I HAVE TO GO TO BED SOON.

WELL, THANKS FOR COMING OVER.

I HAD A GOOD TIME.

YEAH. ME TOO.

"DOWN IN THE WOODS SOMEWHERE A BIRD BEGAN TO SING."

IF I WANTED TO STAY...

NO.

I CAN'T DO IT.

BUT *THEY* MIGHT.

WHO?

THE ONES IN THERE.

THERE'S PEOPLE IN THERE? I THOUGHT YOU SAID IT WAS EMPTY.

IT AIN'T EMPTY. I SAID NOBODY LIVES THERE. DIFFERENT THINGS.

I GOT TO GO NOW...

DEARLY?

"THE RUNT ATE HIS LAST MILKY WAY AND STARED AT THE TUMBLEDOWN BUILDING. THE EMPTY WINDOWS OF THE FARMHOUSE WERE LIKE EYES, WATCHING HIM.

"IT WAS DARKER INSIDE THERE..."

I'LL NEVER GET TO THE SEA. THEY'LL NEVER LET ME.

"... DARKER THAN ANYTHING.

"HE STOPPED AT THE DOORWAY, HESITATING, WONDERING IF THIS WAS WISE.

"HE COULD SMELL DAMP, AND ROT, AND SOMETHING ELSE UNDERNEATH. HE THOUGHT HE HEARD SOMETHING MOVE, DEEP IN THE HOUSE.

"A SHUFFLE, MAYBE. OR A HOP.

"IT WAS HARD TO TELL.

"EVENTUALLY HE WENT INSIDE."

IT WAS A STORY, I'LL SAY THAT FOR IT.

DECEMBER

...I'LL SAY THAT FOR IT.

WHAT HAPPENED NEXT? AFTER HE WENT INTO THE HOUSE?

BETTER NOT TO THINK ABOUT IT.

ANYONE ELSE WANT A TURN?

THEN I THINK WE'RE DONE.

THAT NEEDS TO BE AN OFFICIAL MOTION.

ALL IN FAVOR?

AYE

ALL AGAINST?

THEN I DECLARE THIS MEETING ADJOURNED.

THEY GOT UP FROM THE FIRESIDE AND WALKED AWAY INTO THE WOOD IN ONES AND TWOS AND THREES UNTIL ONLY OCTOBER AND HIS NEIGHBOR REM

YOUR TURN IN THE CHAIR NEXT TIME.

NOVEMBER

I KNOW.

I LIKE YOUR STORIES. MINE ARE ALWAYS TOO DARK.

I DON'T THINK SO. IT'S JUST THAT YOUR NIGHTS ARE LONGER AND YOU AREN'T AS WARM.

PUT IT LIKE THAT AND I FEEL BETTER. I SUPPOSE WE CAN'T HELP WHO WE ARE.

THAT'S THE SPIRIT.

AND THEY TOUCHED HANDS AS THEY WALKED AWAY FROM THE FIRE'S ORANGE EMBERS, TAKING THEIR STORIES WITH THEM BACK INTO THE DARK.

FOR RAY BRADBURY

THE DAY THE
SAUCERS CAME

THAT DAY, THE SAUCERS LANDED, HUNDREDS OF THEM, GOLDEN, SILENT, COMING DOWN FROM THE SKY LIKE GREAT SNOWFLAKES, AND THE PEOPLE OF EARTH STOOD AND STARED AS THEY DESCENDED, WAITING, DRY MOUTHED, TO FIND OUT WHAT WAITED INSIDE FOR US, AND NONE OF US KNEW IF WE WOULD BE HERE TOMORROW, BUT YOU DIDN'T NOTICE IT BECAUSE...

Story by **Neil Gaiman**   Art by **Paul Chadwick**   Lettering by **Gaspar Saladino**

THAT DAY, THE DAY THE SAUCERS CAME, BY SOME COINCIDENCE, WAS THE DAY THAT THE GRAVES GAVE UP THEIR DEAD AND THE ZOMBIES PUSHED UP THROUGH SOFT EARTH, OR ERUPTED, SHAMBLING AND DULL EYED, UNSTOPPABLE, THEY CAME TOWARDS US, THE LIVING, AND WE SCREAMED AND RAN, BUT YOU DID NOT NOTICE THIS BECAUSE...

ON THE SAUCER-ZOMBIE-BATTLING-GODS DAY THE FLOODGATES BROKE AND EACH OF US WAS ENGULFED BY GENIES AND SPRITES OFFERING US WISHES AND WONDERS AND ETERNITIES AND CHARM AND CLEVERNESS AND TRUE BRAVE HEARTS AND POTS OF GOLD WHILE GIANTS FEEFOFUMMED ACROSS THE LAND AND KILLER BEES, BUT YOU HAD NO IDEA OF ANY OF THIS BECAUSE...

HAT DAY, THE SAUCER DAY, THE ZOMBIE DAY,
HE RAGNAROK AND FAIRIES DAY,
HE DAY THE GREAT WINDS CAME
ND SNOWS AND THE CITIES TURNED TO CRYSTAL,
HE DAY ALL PLANTS DIED, PLASTICS DISSOLVED
HE DAY THE COMPUTERS TURNED--
HE SCREENS TELLING US WE WOULD OBEY--
HE DAY
NGELS--DRUNK AND MUDDLED--
TUMBLED FROM THE BARS...